The Great Songs of Stevie Wonder.

Wise Publications
London/New York/Sydney/Cologne

Exclusive Distributors:
Music Sales Limited,
78 Newman Street, London W1P 3LA, England.
Music Sales Pty. Limited,
27 Clarendon Street, Artarmon, Sydney, NSW 2064, Australia.

*Unauthorised reproduction of any part of this publication
by any means including photocopying is an infringement of copyright.*

*This book © Copyright 1983 by Wise Publications
UK ISBN 0.7119.0421.9
UK Order No. AM34596*

*Book designed by Pearce Marchbank Studio.
Cover photography by London Features International.
Compiled by Peter Evans.*

*Music Sales complete catalogue lists thousands of titles
and is free from your local music book shop, or direct from
Music Sales Limited, 78 Newman Street, London W1P 3LA.
Please enclose 25p in stamps for postage.*

*Printed in England by
The Anchor Press Limited, Tiptree, Essex.*

The Great Songs of Stevie Wonder.

I Was Made To Love Her.

Words & Music: Stevie Wonder, Henry Cosby, Lula Mae
Hardaway and Sylvia Moy

2. She's been my inspiration, showed appreciation, for the love I gave her through the years.
   Like a sweet magnolia tree, my love blossoms tenderly, my life grew sweeter through the years.
   I know that my baby loves me, my baby needs me, that's why we made it through the years.
   I was made to love her, worship and adore her. Hey, hey, hey.

3. My baby loves me, my baby needs me, and I know I ain't going nowhere.
   I was knee-high to a chicken, when that love-bug bit me, I had the fever with each passing year.
   Oh, even if the mountain tumbles, if this whole world crumbles, by her side I'll still be standing there.
   'Cause I was made to love her, I was made to live for her. Yeah, hey, hey, hey, ah.

4. I was made to love her, build my world all around her. Hey, hey, hey.
   Oo baby, I was made to please her, you know Stevie ain't gonna leave her no, hey, hey, hey, oo wee baby.
   My baby loves me, my baby needs me. Hey, hey, hey. (fade)

A Place In The Sun.

Words: Ronald Miller
Music: Bryan Wells

Moderately Slow

Like a long lone-ly stream I keep
old dust-y road I keep get

run - nin' towards a dream mov - in' on,_____ mov - in'
wea - ry from the load. Mov - in' on,_____ mov - in'

Signed, Sealed, Delivered I'm Yours.

Words & Music: Stevie Wonder, Syreeta Wright, Lulu Mae
Hardaway and Lee Garrett

Here I am ba - by;

you got my fu - ture in ___ your hands. ___

I've done a lot of fool - ish things, ___ a that I real - ly did - n't mean,

Hey, hey ba - by did - n't I, Oh, ba - by,

3. ___ I'm yours. Oo wee ba - by, you set my soul ___ on fire, ___ that's

To Coda

2. Then that time I went and said goodbye
   Now I'm back and not ashamed to cry, oo baby, here I am
   Signed, sealed, delivered, I'm yours.

3. Seen a lot of things in this old world
   When I touched them they did nothing girl, oo baby, here I am
   Signed, sealed, delivered, I'm yours.

My Cherie Amour.

Words & Music: Stevie Wonder, Henry Cosby and Sylvia Moy

2. In a cafe or sometimes on a crowded street,
   I've been near you but you never noticed me.
   My Cherie Amour, won't you tell me how could you ignore,
   That behind that little smile I wore,
   How I wish that you were mine.

3. Maybe someday you'll see my face among the crowd,
   Maybe someday I'll share your little distant cloud.
   Oh, Cherie Amour, pretty little one that I adore,
   You're the only girl my heart beats for,
   How I wish that you were mine.

Yester-Me, Yester-You, Yesterday.

Words: Ron Miller
Music: Bryan Wells

dream, so did you. Life was warm, love was true.

1st D. S. to 2nd ending
2nd time - D. S. al Fine

Two kids who fol-lowed all the rules, yes-ter-fools, and now, now it

2. Where did it go, that yester-glow
When we could feel the wheel of life turn our way.
Yester-me, yester-you, yester-day.
When I recall what we had,
I feel lost, I feel sad.
With nothing but the mem'ry of yester-love
and now, now it

For Once In My Life.

Words: Ronald Miller.
Music: Orlando Murden.

Superstition.

Words & Music: Stevie Wonder

do all _____ that you can.

Keep me in a day -

dream _____

keep me go-in' strong. ___

You don't wan-na save _____ me, _____

sad _____ is my song. ___

When you be - lieve _____ in things

you don't -

un - der - stand then you suf - fer;

su - per - sti - tion — ain't the way — hey, —

D.S. al Coda 𝄋

—— yeah. Ver - y su - per - sti-

repeat and fade

Coda

You Are The Sunshine Of My Life.

Words & Music: Stevie Wonder

2. You must have known that I was lonely,
   Because you came to my rescue.
   And I know that this must be heaven;
   How could so much love be inside of you? Whoa.

Don't You Worry 'Bout A Thing.

Words & Music: Stevie Wonder

out.   They say— out. _____

When you get

off _____ your trip. ____

— Don't You Wor -ry 'Bout A Thing. _____

Don't You Wor-ry 'Bout   A   Thing.

Ba ——

—— bum —— ba, —— bum ba —— bum, ba —— bum.

Bum bum, bum bum, — bum   bum. ———— Ba ——

Higher Ground.

Words & Music: Stevie Wonder

Moderate rock

Additional Lyrics: *(Repeat last 4 bars as written- sing additional lyrics below)*

Don't you let nobody bring you down. They'll sho' nuff try.
God is gonna show you Higher Ground. He's the only friend you have around.

Boogie On Reggae Woman.

Words & Music: Stevie Wonder

but you dance too fast for me,____
fall ____ deep-ly in love,____

I'd like to make_ love to you so you can make me scream.____
I'd like to see_ you in the raw un-der the stars a-bove.____

Boog-ie on Reg-gae wo-man __ What is wrong ___ with me?
So boog-ie on Reg-gae wo-man ___ What is wrong ___ with you?

Boog-ie on Reg-gae wo-man,____
Boog-ie on Reg-gae wo-man,____

Isn't She Lovely.

Words & Music: Stevie Wonder

Master Blaster (Jammin').

Words & Music: Stevie Wonder

1.2. (Instr. only)
3. Ev- 'ry-one's feel-ing pret-ty;___ it's___ hot-ter than Ju-
4.5.6.7.8. (see additional lyrics)

-ly;___ though___ the world's full of prob-lems,___ they could-n't

41

jam-min', and jam-min', and jam-min!   jam   on._____

jam - min', jam-min', jam-min', jam-   min'

on._____

D.C.

Verse 4:
From the park I hear rhythms;
Marley's hot on the box;
Tonight there will be a party
On the corner, at the end of the block.
Didn't know ... *(To Chorus:)*

Verse 5:
They want us to join their fighting,
But our answer today
Is to let all our worries,
Like the breeze, through our fingers, slip away.

Verse 6:
Peace has come to Zimbabwe;
Third world's right on the one;
Now's the time for celebration,
'Cause we've only just begun.
Didn't know ... *(To Chorus:)*

Verse 7:
You ask me am I happy;
Well, as matter of fact,
I can say that I'm ecstatic,
'Cause we all just made a pact.

Verse 8:
We've agreed to get together;
Joined as children in Jah.
When you're moving in the positive,
Your destination is the brightest star.
Didn't know ... *(To Chorus:)*

Chorus: (vocal ad lib)
Oh, oh, oh, oh, oh, you
(We're in the middle of the makin's
Of the master blaster jammin').
Would be jammin' until the break of dawn.
Don't you stop the music, oh no.
(We're in the middle of the makin's
Of the master blaster jammin').
(Repeat background)
Oh, oh, oh, you
(We're in the middle of the makin's
Of the master blaster jammin').
Would be jammin' until the break of dawn.
I bet you if someone approached you yesterday
To tell you that you would be jammin'
You would not believe it because
You never thought that you would be jammin'.
Oh, oh, oh, oh,
(We're in the middle of the makin's
Of the master blaster jammin').
Jammin' til the break of dawn.
Oh, oh, oh, you may as well believe
What you're feeling because you feel your body jammin'.
Oh, oh, you would be jammin' until the break of dawn.
(We're in the middle of the makin's
Of the master blaster jammin').
(Repeat background)

I Wish.

Words & Music: Stevie Wonder

then my on - ly wor - - ry

was for Christ - mas what would be __ my toy. __

Ev - en though we some - times __

would not get a thing, __ we were hap - py with the __

Tryin' your best to bring the ___ wa-ter to your eyes, ___

think-in' it might stop her ___ from whoop-in' your be-hind. ___ I wish those

days could come back ___ once more. ___ Why did those

days ev - er have ___ to go? ___ I wish those

Brother says he's tellin'
'Bout you playin' doctor with that girl
Just don't tell I'll give you
Anything you want in this whole wide world
Mama gives you money for Sunday school
You trade yours for candy after church is through

Smokin' cigarettes and writing something nasty on the wall (you nasty boy)
Teacher sends you to the principal's office down the hall
You grow up and learn that kinda thing ain't right
But while you were doin' it - it sure felt outta sight

I wish those days could come back once more
Why did those days ev--er have to go?
I wish those days could come back once more
Why did those days ev--er have to go?
'Cause I loved them so.

Superwoman.

Words & Music: Stevie Wonder

52

Sir Duke.

Words & Music: Stevie Wonder

Mus-ic is a world with-in it-self _____ with a
Mus-ic knows it is and al-ways will _____ be one of

lan-guage we all un-der-stand, _____ with an e-qual op-por-
the things that life just won't quit. _____ But here are some of mus-ic's

tu - ni - ty___ for all to sing___ dance and clap their hands _____ but just be-
pi - o - neers,___that time will not___al - low us to for - get _____ for there's

cause a re - cord has a groove___don't make it in the groove but you can
Ba - sie, Mil - ler, Satch-mo, and the king of all, Sir Duke, and with a

tell right a - way at let - ter A___ when the peo - ple start to move.
voice like El - la's ring-in' out___ there's no way the band can lose.

(They)
(You) can feel it all___ o - ver.___ (They)
(You) can feel it all___

54

Do Like You.

Words & Music: Stevie Wonder

1. Since age one, Kei-ta knew he had the

(continue 8va bassa to end)

2nd Verse: Late at night when he was supposed to be sleeping,
You could hear the pitter patter of feet creeping
To where music would play.
To his sister he would say,
Before his father said, "Hey boy,
Get right back in that bed."
Show me...

3rd Verse: Once at school they put on a talent contest
To find out who could really boogie the best.
But his mama said, "No,
Keita's much too young to go."
But his sister said, "Please, let him go
So the world can see."

4th Verse: When they saw him they said he must be crazy.
"Look at him, he ain't nothing but a baby."
But soon as he began
You knew the contest he would win,
Because everyone in the audience
Began to cheer.
Show me...

Lately.

Words & Music: Stevie Wonder

Moderately Slow

1.) Late - ly I have had the strang - est
2.) (see additional lyrics)

feel - ing ___ with no viv - id rea -son here to find.

'cause this time could mean good

bye. ____

time could mean good -

bye, good - bye. ____ Oh,

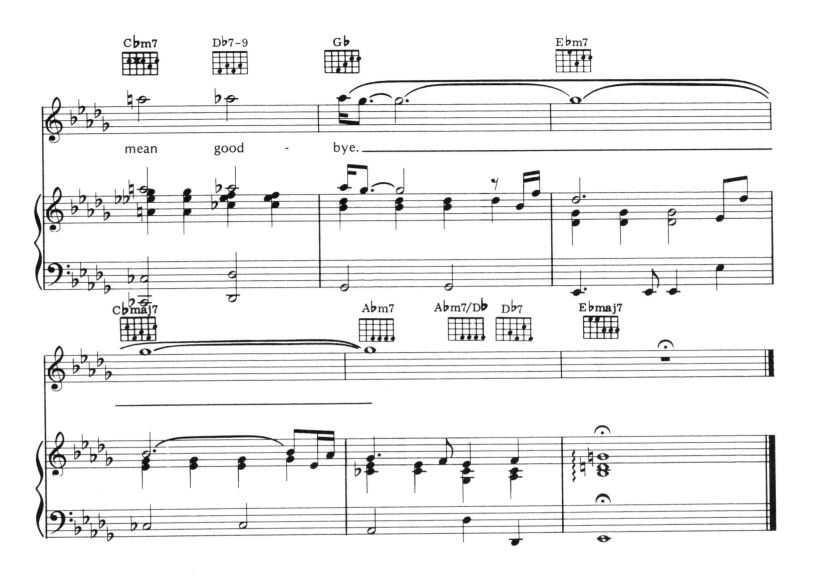

2nd Verse: Lately I've been staring in the mirror,
Very slowly picking me apart;
Trying to tell myself I have no reason
With your heart.
Just the other night while you were sleeping,
I vaguely heard you whisper someone's name.
But when I ask you of the thoughts you're keeping,
You just say nothing's changed.
Well, I'm a man.........etc.

Happy Birthday.

Words & Music: Stevie Wonder

Why has there nev - er been___ a hol - i - day___

where peace is cel - e - brat - ed

all through - out _____ the world? _____

D.S. al Coda

3.) The

Coda

loud___ as ___ you can. Hap - py

hap - py birth - day._____ Hap - py

2nd Verse:

I just never understood
How a man who died for good
Could not have a day that would
Be set aside for his recognition.
Because it should never be,
Just because some cannot see
The dream as clear as he,
That they should make it become an illusion.
And we all know everything
That he stood for time will bring.
For in peace our hearts will sing
Thanks to Martin Luther King.
Happy birthday....

3rd Verse:

The time is overdue
For people like me and you
Who know the way to truth
Is love and unity to all God's children.
It should be a great event,
And the whole day should be spent
In full remembrance
Of those who lived and died
For the oneness of all people.
So let us all begin.
We know that love can win.
Let it out, don't hold it in.
Sing as loud as you can.
Happy birthday...

Recitation
For fade
Ending

We know the key to unity of all people.
It was in the dream that we had so long ago,
That lives in all of the hearts of people
That believe in unity. We will make the
Dream become a reality. I know we will,
Because our hearts tell us so.

Knocks Me Off My Feet.

Words & Music: Stevie Wonder

you ____ with _____ my trou - ble, _____

but there's some-thing 'bout your love _____ that makes me weak ___ and

knocks me off ___ my feet. ___ There's some-thing 'bout your love _____ that